Phonic Readers
AGE 4-6
LEVEL 1

The Three Little Pigs

Autumn
Publishing

Focus on the **p** sound (as in **p**igs) as you read.

Once u**p**on a time, there were three little **p**igs. The **p**igs had a **p**lan. It was a **p**erfect **p**lan.

Let's find a **p**retty new **p**lace to live!

One morning, they said goodbye to their mum, **P**at, and set off along the **p**ath.

path

pegs

pants

plant

pan

Good job

P

3

Focus on the **s** sound (as in **s**traw) as you read.

Sam was the fir**s**t pig. He **s**aw **s**ome **s**traw.

A **s**traw hou**s**e will be **s**uper!

4

When the **s**traw house was finished, **S**am **s**at in the sun.

s

Can you spot these 5 items somewhere in the scene?

Place the stickers from your sticker sheet here as you find each one.

sink

spade

star

straw

sun

Well done

s

Focus on the **w** sound (as in **w**ood) as you read.

Will **w**as the second little pig. He **w**alked and **w**alked until he saw some **w**ood.

What **w**onderful **w**ood to build a house **w**ith.

w

Can you spot these 5 items somewhere in the scene?

Place the stickers from your sticker sheet here as you find each one.

watering can

well

wheat

wheelbarrow

wood

Nice work

w

7

Betty was the third little pig. She **b**uilt her house with **b**ig, strong **b**ricks.

Beautiful.

8

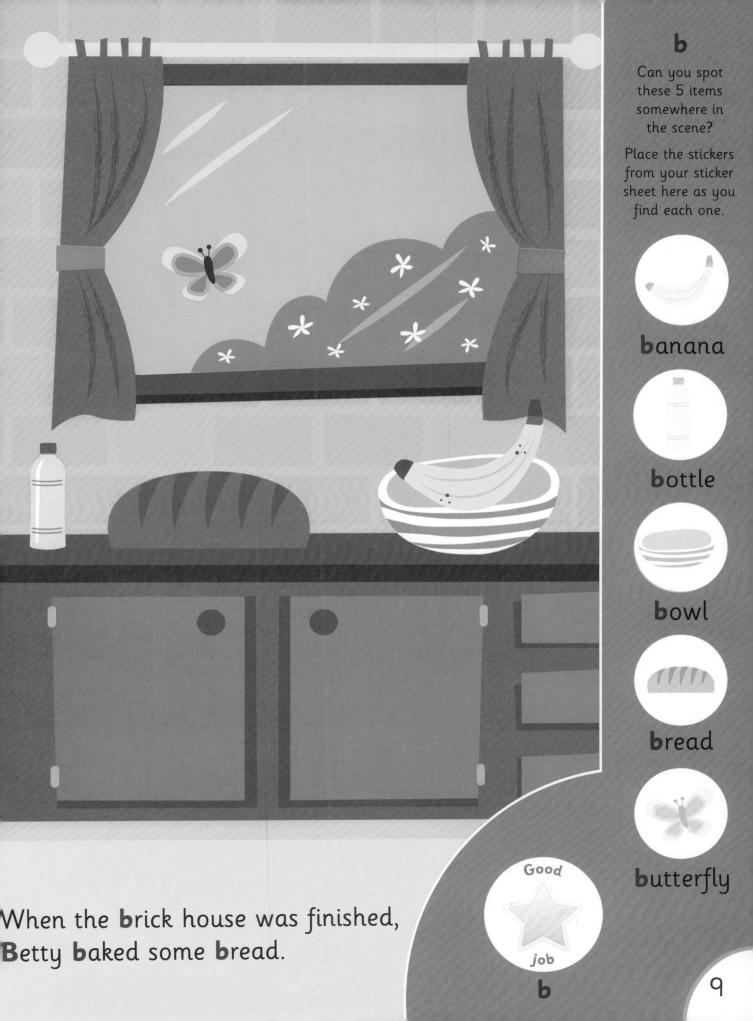

Can you spot these 5 items somewhere in the scene?

Place the stickers from your sticker sheet here as you find each one.

banana

bottle

bowl

bread

butterfly

When the **b**rick house was finished, **B**etty **b**aked some **b**read.

Good

job

b

Focus on the **l** sound (as in little) as you read.

One day, a wolf came along. He **l**iked eating pigs. He went to the **l**ittle house of straw and **l**icked his **l**ips. "**L**ittle pig, **l**ittle pig, **l**et me come in," said the wo**l**f.

Yum, **l**unch would be **l**ovely!

10

l

Can you spot these 5 items somewhere in the scene?

Place the stickers from your sticker sheet here as you find each one.

ladder

lemon

lick

list

letters

Well done

l

11

Focus on the i sound (as in chin) as you read.

"No, not by the hairs on my chinny-chin-chin. I will not let you in", said Sam Pig.

"Well I'll huff and I'll puff until I blow your house in," replied the wolf.

The wolf r**a**n after S**a**m Pig. **A**t last, they both **a**rrived **a**t the house of wood.

S**a**m r**a**n to the b**a**ck. The wolf s**a**t on the front door m**a**t. "Little pig, little pig, it's time I got f**a**t," said the big, b**a**d wolf.

Focus on the **a** sound (as in **a**pple) as you read.

14

"By my knobbly nose I'm not having that!" said Will Pig.

But the wolf blew down the new house until there was nearly nothing left.

Focus on the n sound (as in nose) as you read.

16

Pages 22-23

Pages 24-25

Reward stars

Good
job

Well
done

Nice
work

Good
job

Well
done

Nice
work

Good
job

Well
done

Nice
work

Good
job

Well
done

Nice
work

Sticker Sounds

Page 27

hen

watering can

ladder

n

Can you spot these 5 items somewhere in the scene?

Place the stickers from your sticker sheet here as you find each one.

needle

nest

newspaper

nose

nurse

Well done

n

The wolf ran **h**ard after the pigs. They all **h**eaded for the **h**ouse of bricks.

Inside, Betty was **h**aving **h**ot tea. The **h**ungry wolf **h**ammered on the door.

Little pig, little pig, I'll **h**uff your house down!

Focus on the **h** sound (as in **h**ot) as you read.

18

Can you spot these 5 items somewhere in the scene?

Place the stickers from your sticker sheet here as you find each one.

hammer

helmet

hat

hen

honey

Nice work

h

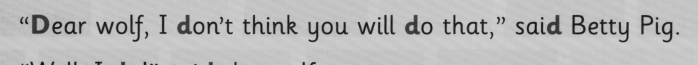

"**D**ear wolf, I **d**on't think you will **d**o that," sai**d** Betty Pig.

"Well, I **d**o!" sai**d** the wolf.
He huffe**d** an**d** puffe**d**. He puffe**d** an**d** huffe**d**.

Focus on
the **d** sound
(as in **d**og)
as you read.

20

Can you spot these 5 items somewhere in the scene?

Place the stickers from your sticker sheet here as you find each one.

bed

dress

dog

doll

drum

Good

job

d

Focus on the c sound (as in cat) as you read.

The wolf could not control his hunger any more.

He climbed onto the roof and came down the chimney.

I will **c**ook you and eat you with **c**arrots and **c**abbage!

23

Focus on the **o** sound (as in h**o**t) as you read.

The wolf g**o**t a shock. The three little pigs were n**o**t waiting at the b**o**tt**o**m.

Instead, the wolf fell into a p**o**t **o**f h**o**t water. SPL**OS**

Hot!
Hot!
Hot!

o

Can you spot these 5 items somewhere in the scene?

Place the stickers from your sticker sheet here as you find each one.

socks

pot

box

frog

log

The wolf ran **o**ff.
The pigs laughed a l**o**t, and were n**o**t scared **o**f the wolf again.

Nice work

o

25

First Letter Lines

Follow the lines to join the pictures to the correct words, then say the sound each one starts with.

sun

pig

apple

Rhyming Pictures

Match up each picture on the left to one that rhymes with it on the right.

pig

sink

bat

brick

stick

hat

wig

pink

Sticker Sounds

Find a sticker from your sticker sheet that starts with the same sound as each of these pictures.

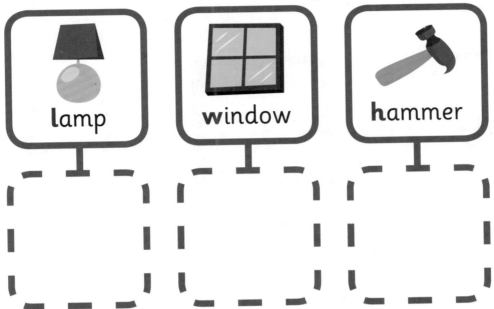

lamp   **w**indow   **h**ammer

Letter Jumble

How many times can you see the letter **p**, as in **p**ig, **p**ants and **p**lant?

Picture Match

Can you join up each picture with the letter it starts with?

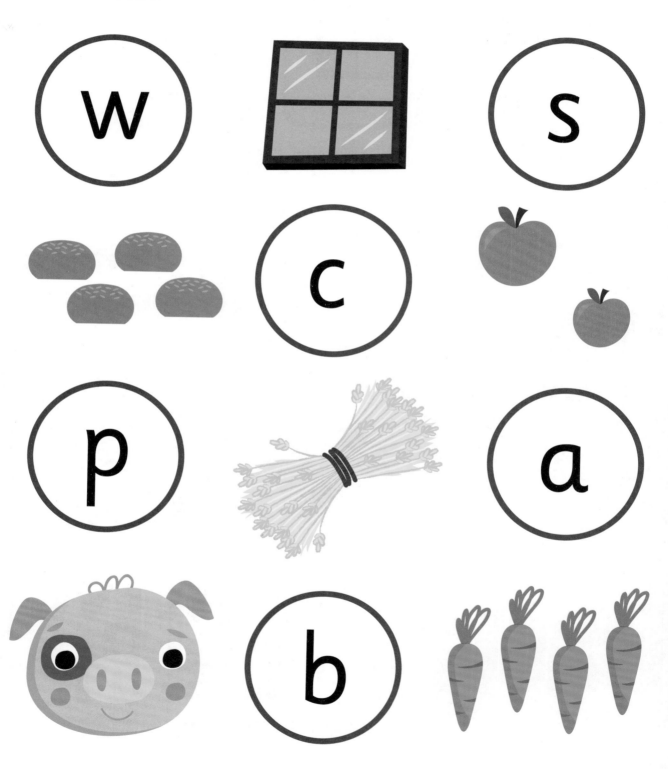

Say the Sounds

Look at the picture and say all the things that start with the **s** sound, as in **s**un.

Tell a Story

Look at the pictures and tell the story from memory.
What sounds can you remember?

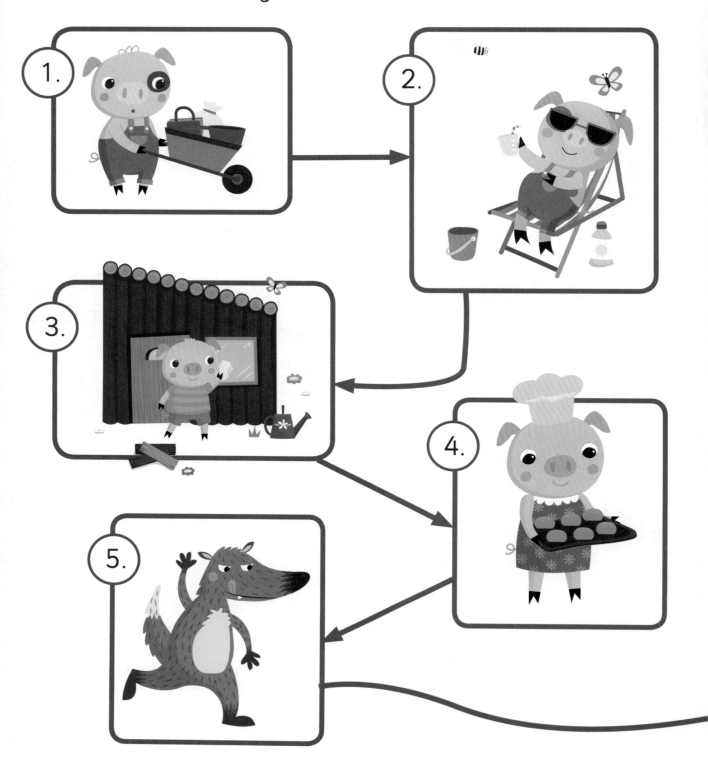

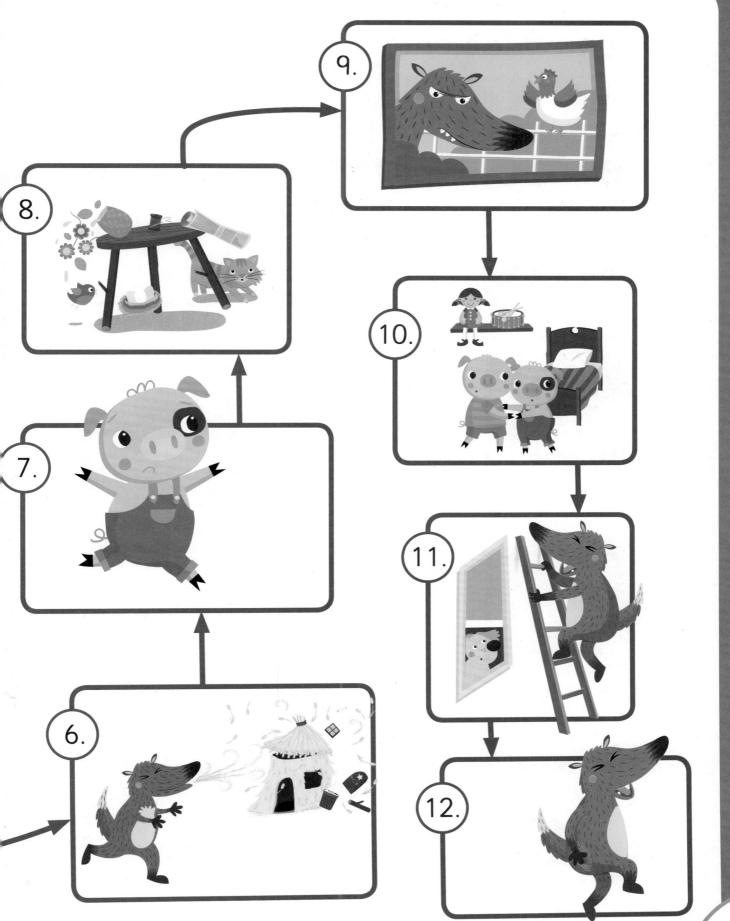

Phonic Moments

Fill in the key sound words for each picture below.
What happened in these parts of the story?